THE BEST OF HERMAN

JIM UNGER

GRUB STREET • LONDON

Published by Grub Street,
The Basement, 10 Chivalry Road,
London SWll lHT

Copyright © 1993 by Jim Unger
distributed internationally by
Universal Press Syndicate

The moral right of the author has been asserted

British Library Cataloguing in Publication Data
Unger, Jim
Very Best of Herman
I. Title
741.5

ISBN 0-948817-84-4

Printed and bound in Great Britain by Biddles Ltd,
Guildford and Kings Lynn

**"If you insist on laughing, sir, I must
ask you to browse in the humor section."**

"There's absolutely *nothing*
on TV tonight!"

"That's the last time we'll
use this hospital!"

"What did you *expect*
to find in oxtail soup?"

"I'll just let them help themselves."

"What does that sound like to you?"

"I asked you what you wanted for lunch and you said, 'Surprise me.'"

"Got a dog to fit that?"

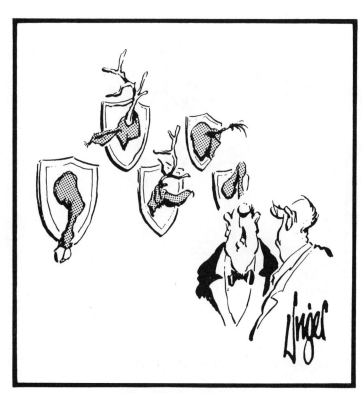

"I hit it with the truck."

"I'm your new secretary. Am I an
hour late or 23 hours early?"

"Your scalp's very dry."

"Got any nice gift-wrapping paper?"

"I can't see him without
an appointment!"

"Don't keep ducking."

"Open up! I want to take a
look down your throat."

"Now don't go running off 'til
I find out where we are."

"Be careful with the wine. I had
trouble getting the cork out."

"Didn't you pay the cable TV bill?"

"I got 6 percent in math.
Is that good or bad?"

"Did you try the vertical hold?"

**"How do you get these
little bottles in a typewriter?"**

"Ralphy...what did you use to get
that new glue off your finger?"

"Have you heard that expression,
'You are what you eat'?"

"People are beginning to complain about
too much violence on cave walls."

"One of everything."

"I wish I could lay around in bed all day every time I had a sore throat."

"Your teeth are fantastic, but your gums have to come out."

"Of course it's half eaten! You said
you wanted the chef's salad."

"You can go home for Christmas."

"Don't light that in here."

**"So this is the best movie your
sister has ever seen."**

"Have you done the north slope?"

"You're an hour late! Don't blame me
if your cheese sandwich is ruined."

"It never ceases to amaze
me what people throw away."

"And don't give me any of
those local anesthetics.
Get me the imported stuff."

"How much to the airport if I drive?"

"Well, you knew we had only
one tree when you bought it."

"This is new. . . . 'mega-puncture.'"

"This is the last one he painted."

"I told you never to get between
Mother and a dessert trolley."

"The guy across the street wants
to know what you're cooking."

"That too tight?"

"Did your mother say you could
build a nuclear device?"

"Well, if it's the wrong number,
why did you answer the phone,
you idiot? Now I've lost my coin."

"Here we are, Mount Everest.
I need 29,000 feet of rope."

"She said if I don't finish the
fence in time, I won't be able
to go to her sister's wedding."

"Show me what to press if I want to record a movie after I've gone to bed."

"I use this one when it's raining."

"I didn't ask you if you smoked. I said, 'Do you need any matches?'"

"They hung this mirror upside down."

"I need both hands for turning!"

"Here we go! Step one: Take off your shirt."

"We can't stand here all
day. It must have jammed."

"Table for three."

"Ear, nose, and throat!"

"I can let you have
those for half price."

"I need one more gallon
of that ceiling white."

"Something just landed on my back!"

"I said, take the *lock* off!"

"I spilled my coffee
on the computer!"

"OK, that's enough for one day.
I'll see you next Tuesday."

"Is it too tight across the shoulders?"

"Haven't you got one in English?"

"We ate at home, so we just want
to check how much we saved."

"Fourteen years old and still playful."

"We've decided on a small wedding. I'm not going."

"I told you to call an electrician."

"I had no choice. My wife thinks hunting is cruel."

"I thought you said you were an airline pilot."

"This should hold it!"

"You shouldn't carry all this cash.
Why don't you open an account?"

"Are we still hiring minorities?"

"I wonder why they make these
finger bandages so long?"

"Dropping out of school
never done me no harm."

"I've seen it before. He's changing into a butterfly."

"Will you keep the noise down! We're trying to have a party next door."

"No, sir. This is not a Greek restaurant.
You have the menu upside down."

"Is your wife still taking singing lessons?"

"Why would I take your pipe? Have you looked in the kitchen?"

"I can't remember: Are accountants 'left brain' or 'right brain'?"

"You fell off the operating table."

"D'you buy used cats?"

"There's someone out here
waiting to use the phone."

"Mrs. Baxter, I don't think
things are going to work out."

"How can I find anything when you keep leaving this razor all over the bathroom?"

"Can you cut me a star-shaped piece of glass to fit that hole?"

"I think I'll give it a shot
on my own today, Bernie."

"Your honor, before the jury retires to reach
a verdict my client wishes to present each of
them with a little gift of jewelry."

"If you find a pork chop in your soup, it belongs to table nine."

"I'm putting you down as 'potential donor material.'"

"Now that you've cut off my electricity, how do you expect me to find my checkbook in the dark?"

"Joyce, give this guy a second cup of coffee. He found my car keys."

"Your boss didn't want you to lay here worrying about the work piling up, so he fired you."

"Use your fingers."

"Mr. White is here for his annual checkup, doctor."

"D'you think you'll be writing a
book about it after you get out?"

"Quick, drink this! It'll
settle your stomach."

"I hear you're looking for
an aggressive salesman."

"I lost track of my age years ago,
but I think I'm about 22."

"I'm—fine—how—are—you?"

"When are you going to face the fact that you're a lousy pickpocket?"

"I'm not going to give you a tip. I don't like to hurt people's feelings."

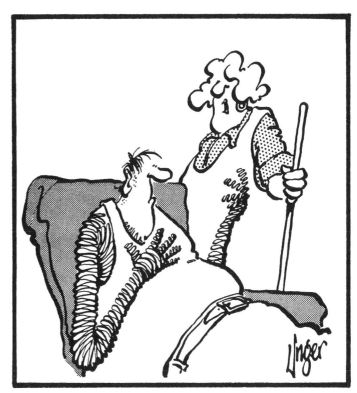

"I told you not to lay in the bath all afternoon!"

"Dear Pinkie: Having a wonderful
time in the south of France."

"You're quite a puzzle, aren't you?"

"Detective Parker, zoo patrol."

"If you can spare the time, Williams,
I'd like to see you in my office."

"Here . . . tell your mother we're out. She won't believe me."

"I see the old dollar's taken another beating."

**"You should stay off that left
foot for a couple of days."**

"I need 148 get-well cards."

"I'm starting my vacation tomorrow,
so I'll leave you 14 newspapers."

"I caught it in a copier machine."

"Don't keep changing your mind."

"You won't find a job
in the sports section!"

"Does that say, 'Learn
to read in seven days'?"

"The TV keeps switching
back to 'Wild Kingdom'!"

"We were finding it very
hot in here, Warden."

"I left the circus 17 years ago
and I think I still miss it!"

"I *know* the tablecloth's dirty.
Don't forget, this place has
been open since 1963."

"Which parent do you want to sign it: my
natural father, my stepfather, my mother's
third husband, my real mother or my natural
father's fourth wife who lives with us?"

"Go to sleep. Everybody has one
foot bigger than the other."

"Dougie, have we got these in coral pink?"

"I guess I'll plead not guilty just
to get the old ball rolling."

"I hope you know your stuff.
I'm a very weak swimmer."

"Rub this on your feet three
times a day, during meals."

"I'll have two eggs
and some b-a-c-o-n."

"If he had six wives, how come
there was no Henry the Ninth?"

"You didn't fill it up, did you?"

"It's for you, Mildred."

"So anyway, I thought, you won't be back
for 10 minutes. I'll grab a hot dog."

"Unless I'm mistaken, you had a pretty hefty pay hike in 1967."

"When are you gonna start facing reality?"

"This guy wants to know
if we deliver to Africa."

"He's out! Can I take a message?"

"How d'you expect me to remember your birthday? I was only a year old."

"And now for a look at the latest picture from a weather satellite."

"These are for you in court.
We're going for 'insanity'."

"I told you it was supposed
to go around your neck."

"Clamp!"

"Who's having the raw herring?"

"Old Rex has been in the family for
as far back as I can remember."

"What happened to my sun screen?"

"We need something fast
for about 10 minutes."

"Mrs. Rodriguez, next Monday I
want you to stand in for me at the
annual stockholders meeting."

"Do you know if you want Dr. Humblestone the skin specialist or Dr. Humblestone the gynecologist?"

"You're supposed to let wine breathe."

**"Come on. You were all
excited when you saw it on TV."**

**"Ladies and gentlemen...
the gride and broom."**

"Five cans of ceiling white."

"Her idea of a balanced diet is
four pounds of chocolate with
four pounds of cake."

"A vote for me is a vote
for the small businessman."

"Breathe out."

"Don't bother to leave a tip.
I had one of your sausages."

"OK, don't start showing off!"

"Helen, turn to Channel 22, 'World of Magic.'"

"You say you were inside robbing the bank and someone stole your car?"

"I could literally double my income with a 20-foot ladder."

"Couldn't he wait?"

"I just want to double-check your order before I go. You did say 'Atlantic cod,' didn't you?"

"Arnold, will you please stand away from that on-off switch?"

"Sure, come over to dinner one evening. You can have mine."

"Make sure he pays cash."

"I didn't bring my glasses. Does that say you've been pardoned?"

"Personally, I think it's all these chemicals they spray on the fruit."

"Would you prefer to eat inside?"

"I think you'll find my test results
are a pretty good indication of
your abilities as a teacher."

"You left this refrigerator
open again."

"I'm sorry, sir, that's not hand luggage."

"The computer handles
all our applications."

"D'you want 'Outpatients' or 'Emergency'?"

"If you're so smart, how come the world was in such a mess before I got here?"

"Can't you make less
noise when you eat?"

"You're certainly a front-runner
for the store detective job."

"Two years is a long
time to have jet lag."

"Think back . . . two years ago
. . . you sold me a gerbil."

"I can't bring the car
back 'til low tide."

"I should fire you, but I don't believe
in mixing business with pleasure."

"Is this the first time you've had your eyes tested?"

"Did you tell the cat he could have my striped shirt?"

"Luckily, our honeymoon suite
had a TV in the bedroom."

OTHER CARTOON BOOKS AVAILABLE FROM GRUB STREET

THE 99 DON'TS
A Guide to Unrecommendable Practises
Steven Appleby and Kjartan Poskitt
£3.99

THE 122 TURN-OFFS
A Catalogue of Unnerving Encounters
Steven Appleby and Kjartan Poskitt
£3.99

LARRY ON LARRY
Britain's best loved and best known
cartoonist collects together a personal
selection of his work.
£6.99

PIGSWILL AND OTHER DIETS
Giles Pilbrow
£3.99

CAUGHT SHORT
89 Ways to Pee in Public Without
Being Spotted
Brian Heaton
£3.99

101 USES OF A CONDOM
Russell Jones
£2.95

ISN'T PROGRESS WONDERFUL?
The First Book of Eco-humour
Stan Eales
£7.50

CASHTOONS
Stan Eales
£3.99

MOUTHFOOL
A Gourmet Collection of Culinary
Cartoons
Enzo Apicella
£5.99

FOR A COMPLETE LIST OF ALL
OUR PUBLICATIONS WRITE TO:

**GRUB STREET,
THE BASEMENT,
10 CHIVALRY ROAD,
LONDON SW11 1HT**